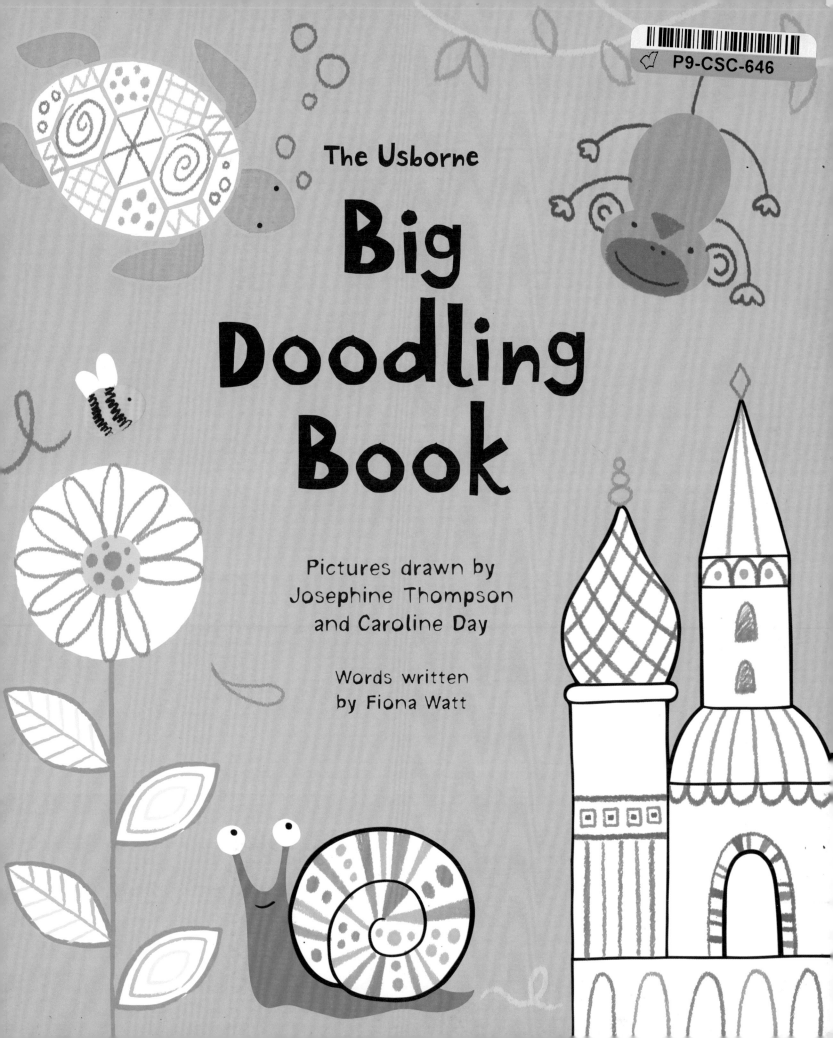

The Usborne
Big Doodling Book

Pictures drawn by
Josephine Thompson
and Caroline Day

Words written
by Fiona Watt

Do I have spots...Yes Do I have stripes...Yes

...and I need some more legs.

Turn the shapes into bugs.

Doodle lots of little legs...

...and add spots, stripes and swirls.

3

Baa!

Doodle lots of curly wool on the sheep...

...and draw wavy patterns on the goats.

Baa!

5

Doodle patterns on the monster trucks.

Add some dust or smoke.

VroOOOOoom!

VroOOoom!

Doodle wavy feathers and wings...

and turn the green shapes into leaves, too.

Twit-twoooo

9

Doodle stripes for tigers, curly manes for lions...

...or spots for a leopard.

Roar!

11

Fill the white shapes with lots of bright patterns.

Lots of animals' heads...

MeOw!

Woof woof!

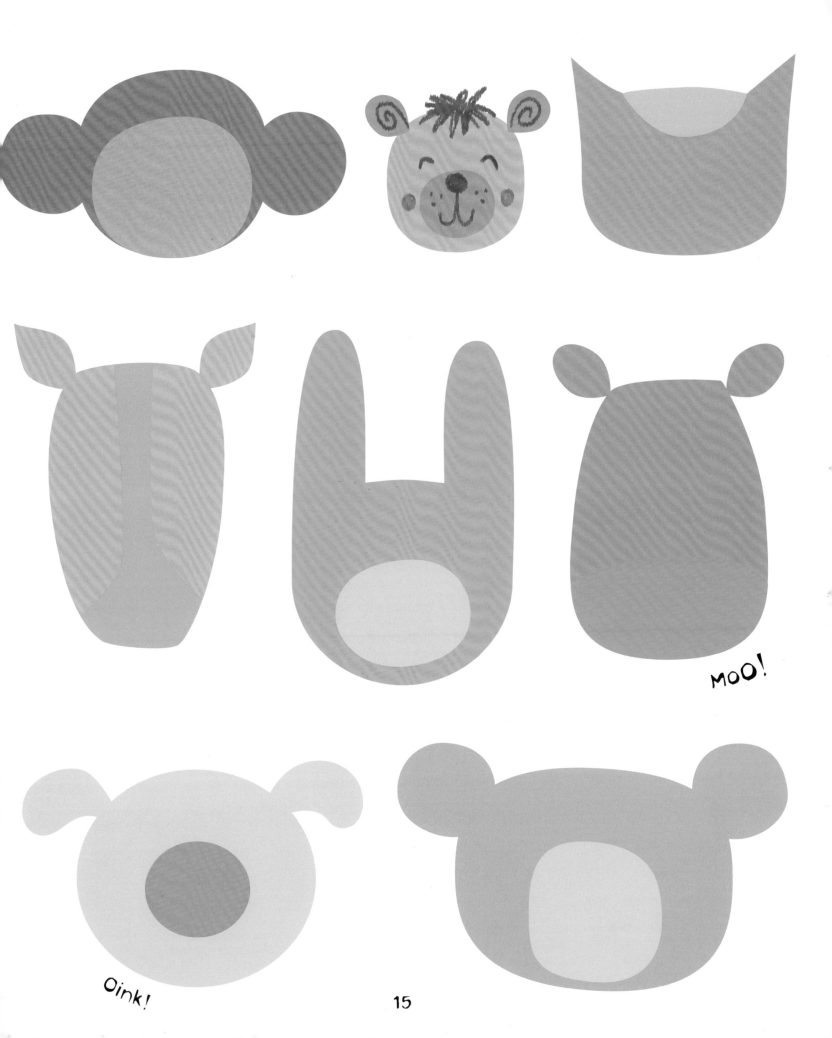

Oink!

15

MoO!

Decorate the flowers and doodle stripes on the bees.

Bzzzzz

Bzzzzz

Doodle lots of scaly patterns.

18

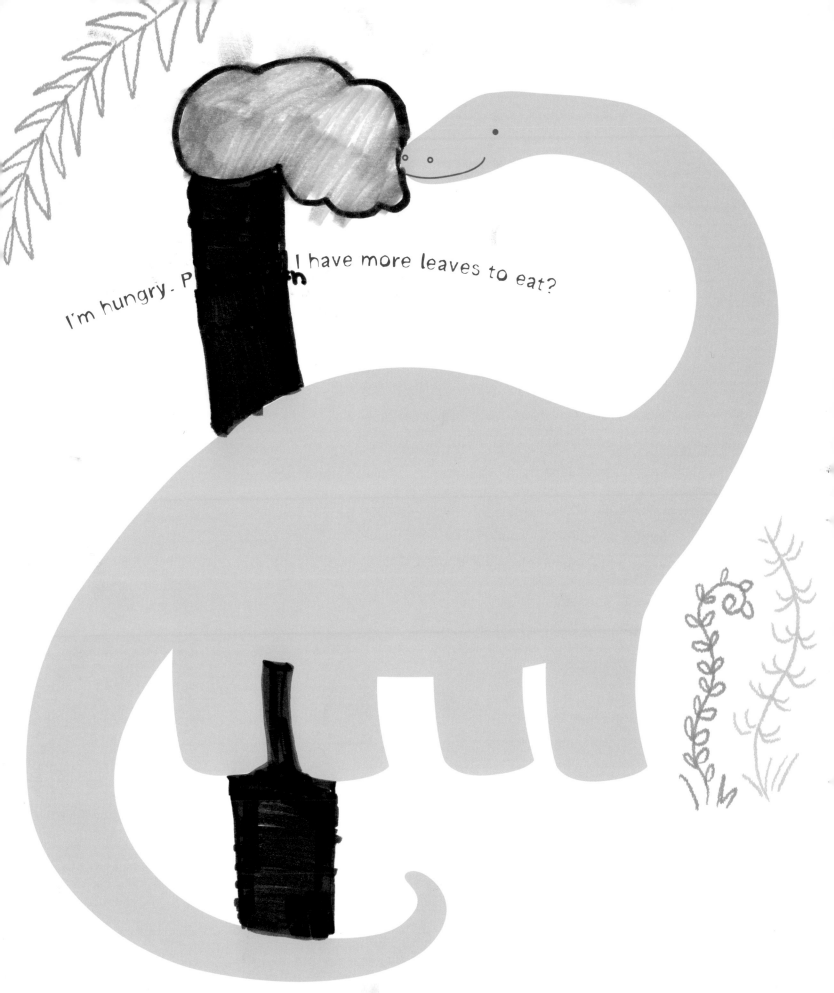

I'm hungry. P... I have more leaves to eat?

We need some scales to help us swim.

20

splish...

splash...

splosh!

21

Doodle lots of dials, lights and patterns on the robots.

BLEEP!

BIP!

BEEP!

23

We'd love to have some eyes, wings and feathery patterns.

What patterns could you use to brighten up these plain buildings?

Turn these shapes into gingerbread men and women.

We would like lots of wiggly legs...

...and we need some patterns on our legs.

31

Where are the bunnies' ears and tails?

Give them lots of carrots, too.

Doodle spots and stripes on the frogs...

...and patterns on the snakes.

Doodle a tongue on each one. Sssssss!

Turn the shapes into penguins having fun in the snow.

Doodle some hats to keep them warm.

Wheeeeeeee!

Doodle delicate patterns on the elephants.

Sploosh

Tweet

Oh dear! The **patterns** on these clothes have been washed off. Please help.

Fill the spaces with more wet clothes.

41

Doodle swirls and curls...

...and dots and spots.

Turn the brown shapes into monkeys ...

oo..oo..ee..ee

...and doodle more leaves on the tree, too.

45

Can you fill these empty shapes?

Then fill this empty space with shapes of your own.

Doodle lines and dots on the bats' wings...

... and draw faces on the pumpkins.

49

Doodle patterns on the shells, sea creatures and seaweed.

Cock-a-doodle-dooO!

Give the hens and chicks eyes, beaks and wings....

52

...and add orange legs, too.

Cheep!

Cheep!

Cheep!

Doodle on these circles to turn them into faces...

Sleepy

Oooo!

Yo-ho-ho!

Don't cry...

...and add some more faces to fill the empty spaces.

Doodle patterns on the turtles' shells, heads and flippers.

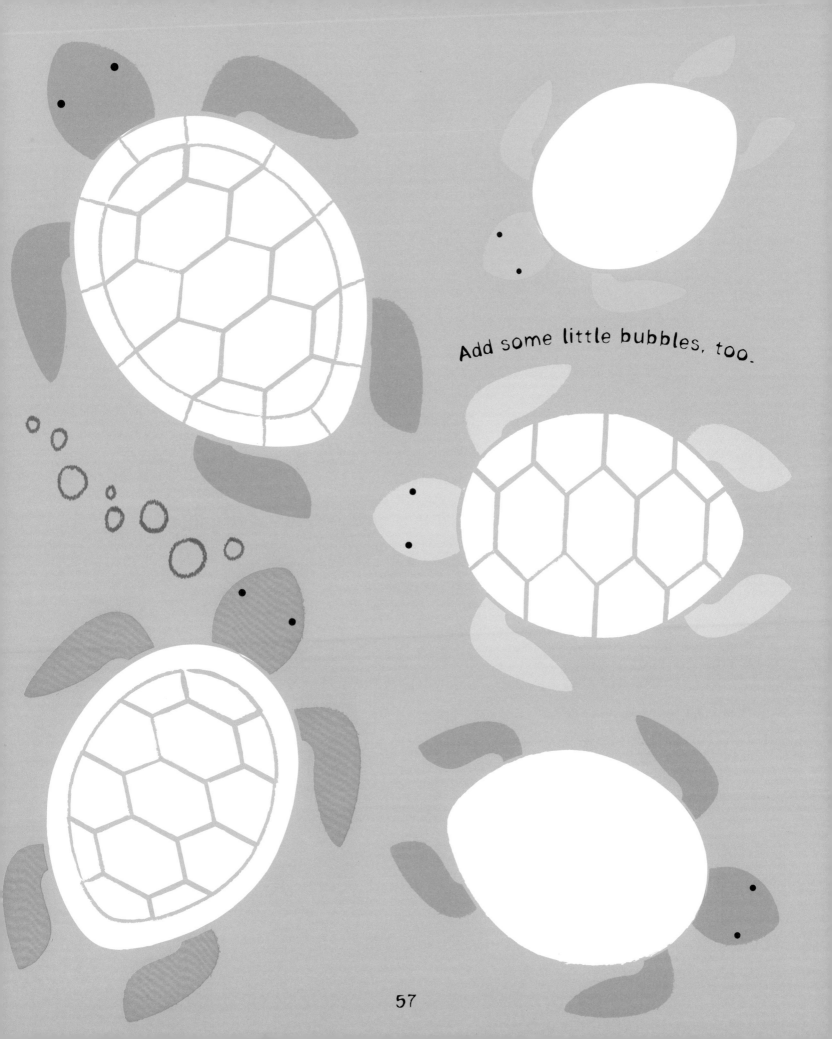

Add some little bubbles, too.

Doodle on the flags and towers...

...and draw lots more flags and another tower, too.

Turn these blobs into monsters.

These houses need windows and doors...

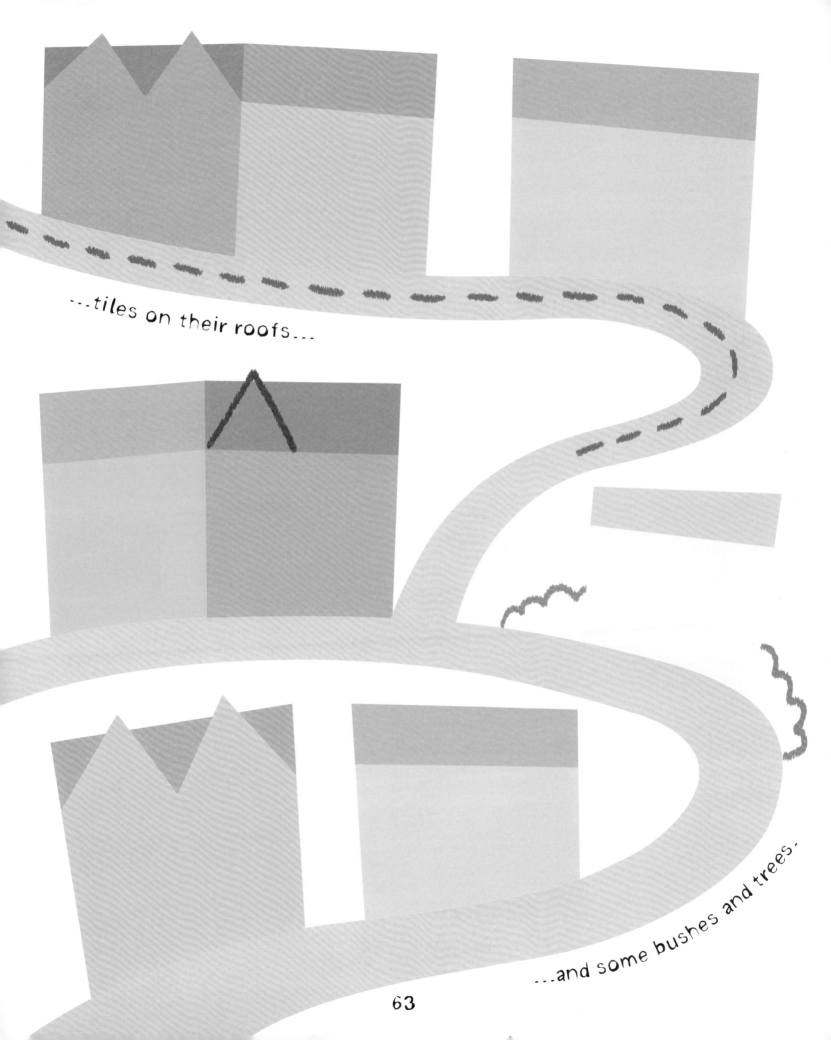

...tiles on their roofs...

...and some bushes and trees.

63

Doodle flames along the rockets' trails

Fill the stars with yellow.

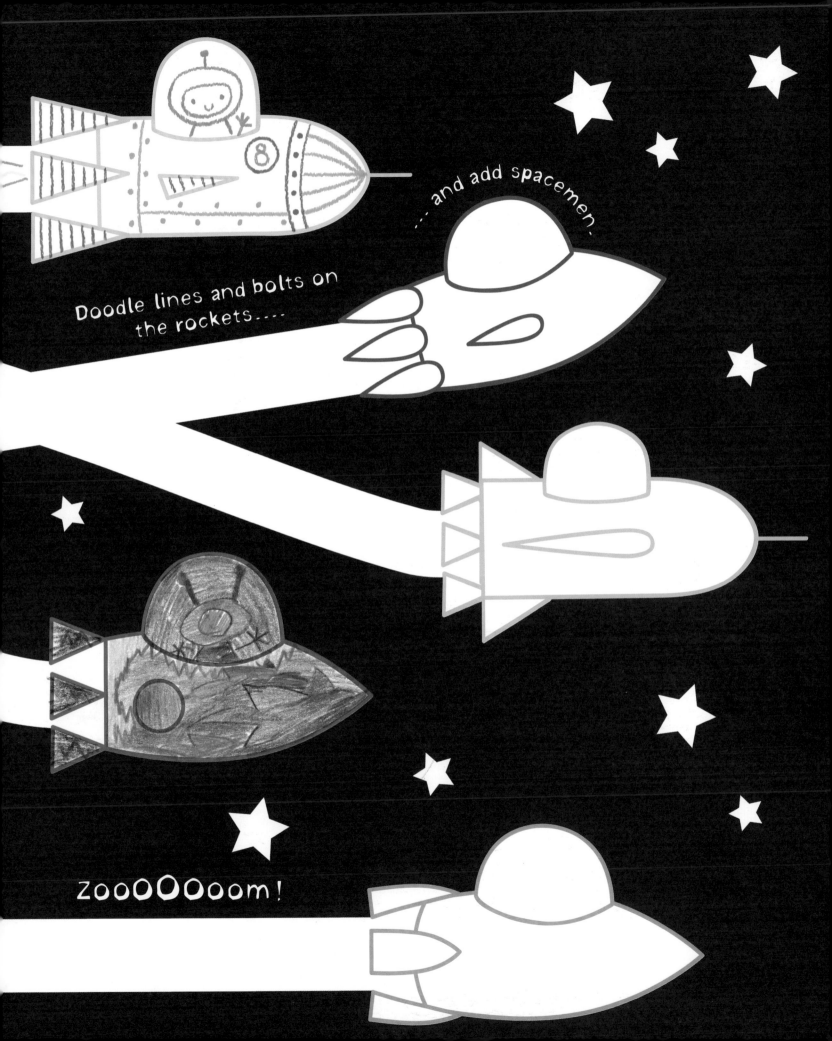

Doodle lines and bolts on the rockets....

...and add spacemen.

ZoooOOOoom!

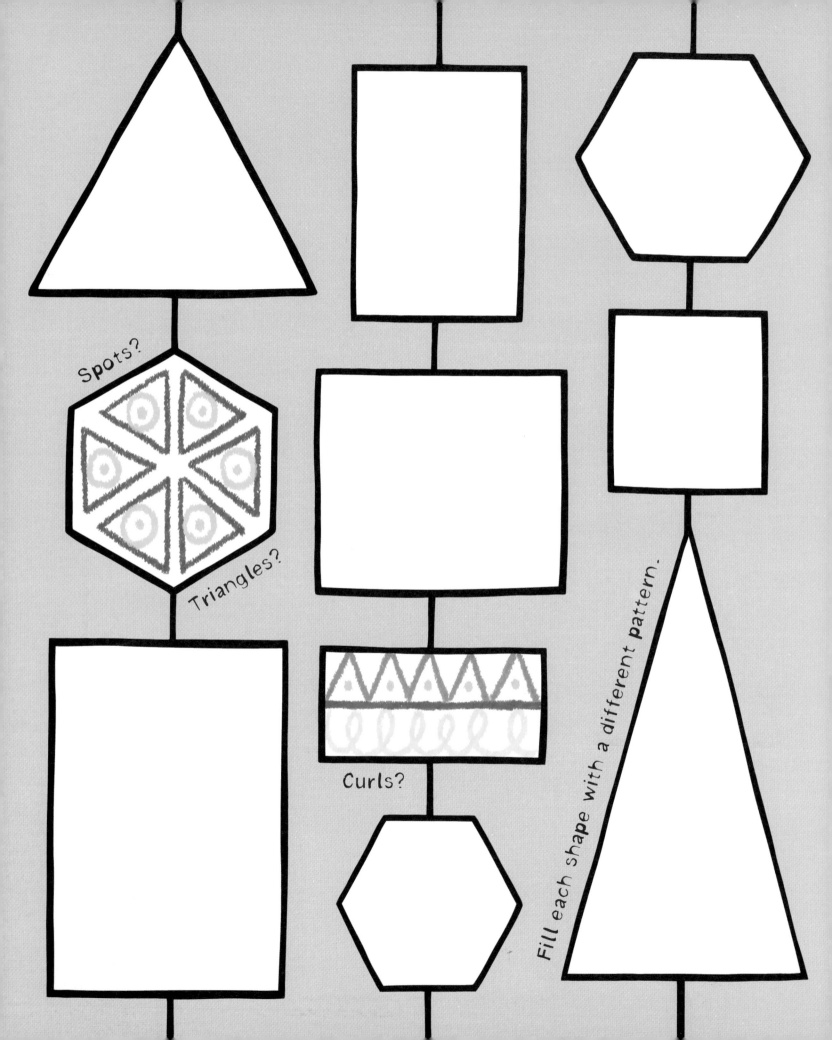

Spots?

Triangles?

Curls?

Fill each shape with a different pattern.

Loops?

Dots?

Most of us need some spots.

Munch munch

Doodle more leaves for this hungry giraffe.

69

Turn these white shapes into snowmen.

I'm freeeeezing!

I'm cold, too!

Doodle faces on the babies...

...then decorate their quilts.

Night...night...

Doodle lots of bright spots on the toadstools.

Turn these shapes into mice and lumps of cheese...

Squeak!

...and these shapes into children playing.

Turn each circle into a sun with a happy face.

Doodle raindrops, snowflakes and flashes of lightning.

80

Doodle a face and eight legs on each spider.

Add curls, lines and zigzag fur, and looping lines on the acorns.

How many balls can the seals balance on their noses?

...and doodle patterns, too.

Finish the fence...

Doodle more buildings ...

...and add some more trees.

...and draw more cars.

Add spiky teeth and fins to these hungry sharks.

Snap!

Fill the empty shapes with different patterns.

Doodle faces on the **people** on the train.

Add some coal to the empty wagon.

Add more faces in the empty windows.

Toot..toot

Our shells need some lines and spots...

...and we need lots of spikes.

Doodle decorations on the tree... ...and add lots of little lights.